Disney.

This book belongs to

Written by Bonnie Brooke
Illustrated by Isidre Monés

Disney
Bambi

Hide-and-Seek

"Hello, Thumper!"
said Bambi.
"Hi-ya, Bambi!"
said Thumper.
"Whatcha wanna play?"

"Well," said Bambi,
"how about . . ."
"Hide-and-Seek!"
cried Thumper.

"One, two, three, four . . ." counted Bambi while Thumper scampered off to hide.

"Here I come!" called Bambi.
"Now, where could he be . . .?"
Aha! Was that a bunny behind
the bush?

No. It was Momma Mouse
hiding her napping babies.
"Ssh!" she warned.

Was that Thumper up in a tree?

No. It was a squirrel
hiding nuts.

Was that Thumper making a noise by the stream?

No. It was a frog snuggled up
in a water lily.
"Ribbit!"

Was that a bunny tail behind
the log?

No. It was a woodpecker looking for bugs. Tap, tap, tap!

Bambi lay down to rest.
Where could Thumper be?

Suddenly, a clump of flowers said, "Achoo!"

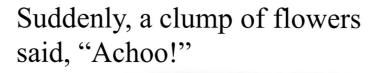

"That's called Hide-and-Sneeze!" giggled Bambi.

"Let's play again!"
laughed Thumper.

The End